ATOMS, MOLECULES & ELEMENTS
Matter & Energy Series

● ● ● ● ● ● ● ● ● ● ● ● ● ● ● ● ● ● ● ●

Written by George Graybill, Ph. D.

GRADES 5 - 8
Reading Levels 3 - 4

Classroom Complete Press
P.O. Box 19729
San Diego, CA 92159
Tel: 1-800-663-3609 / Fax: 1-800-663-3608
Email: service@classroomcompletepress.com

www.classroomcompletepress.com

ISBN-13: 978-1-55319-371-5
ISBN-10: 1-55319-371-7

© 2007

Permission to Reproduce

Critical Thinking Skills

Atoms, Molecules & Elements

	Skills For Critical Thinking	Reading Comprehension							Hands-on Activities
		Section 1	Section 2	Section 3	Section 4	Section 5	Section 6	Section 7	
LEVEL 1 Knowledge	• List Details/Facts	✓	✓					✓	
	• Recall Information	✓	✓			✓	✓	✓	
	• Match Vocab. to Definitions	✓	✓			✓			
	• Define Vocabulary			✓	✓	✓	✓		
	• Label Diagrams							✓	✓
	• Recognize Validity (T/F)	✓	✓	✓	✓	✓	✓	✓	
LEVEL 2 Comprehension	• Demonstrate Understanding	✓	✓	✓	✓	✓	✓	✓	✓
	• Explain Scientific Causation		✓	✓		✓	✓		
	• Rephrasing Vocab. Meaning			✓					
	• Describe			✓	✓	✓		✓	
	• Classify into Scientific Groups	✓		✓	✓			✓	
LEVEL 3 Application	• Application to Own Life		✓	✓		✓			
	• Model Scientific Process	✓				✓	✓		✓
	• Organize and Classify Facts	✓		✓		✓	✓	✓	✓
	• Utilize Alternative Research Tools								✓
LEVEL 4 Analysis	• Distinguish Roles/Meanings								
	• Make Inferences	✓				✓	✓	✓	✓
	• Draw Conclusions Based on Facts Provided	✓			✓	✓	✓		✓
	• Classify Based on Facts Researched		✓		✓	✓			
LEVEL 5 Synthesis	• Compile Research Information		✓		✓	✓			✓
	• Design and Application			✓					✓
	• Create and Construct			✓		✓	✓		✓
	• Imagine Self in Scientific role								✓
LEVEL 6 Evaluation	• State and Defend an Opinion				✓	✓	✓		✓
	• Justify Choices for Research Topics								
	• Defend Selections and Reasoning					✓			✓

Based on Bloom's Taxonomy

Atoms, Molecules & Elements CC4505

Contents

• • • • • • • • • • • • • • • • •

FREE! 6 Bonus Activities!

3 EASY STEPS to receive your 6 Bonus Activities!
- • Go to our website:
  www.classroomcompletepress.com\bonus
- • Click on item CC4505 – Atoms, Molecules & Elements
- • Enter pass code CC4505D

Assessment Rubric

• • • • • • • • • • • • • • • • • • •

Atoms, Molecules & Elements

Student's Name: _____ Assignment: _____ Level: _____

	Level 1	Level 2	Level 3	Level 4
Understanding Concepts	Demonstrates a limited understanding of concepts. Requires teacher intervention.	Demonstrates a basic understanding of concepts. Requires little teacher intervention.	Demonstrates a good understanding of concepts. Requires no teacher intervention.	Demonstrates a thorough understanding of concepts. Requires no teacher intervention.
Analysis & Application of Key Concepts	Limited application and interpretation in activity responses	Basic application and interpretation in activity responses	Good application and interpretation in activity responses	Strong application and interpretation in activity responses
Creativity and Imagination	Limited creativity and imagination applied in projects and activities	Some creativity and imagination applied in projects and activities	Satisfactory level of creativity and imagination applied in projects and activities	Beyond expected creativity and imagination applied in projects and activities
Application of Own Interests	Limited application of own interests in independent or group environment	Basic application of own interests in independent or group environment	Good application of own interests in independent or group environment	Strong application of own interests in independent or group environment

STRENGTHS:

WEAKNESSES:

NEXT STEPS:

Teacher Guide

Our resource has been created for ease of use by both TEACHERS and STUDENTS alike.

Introduction

This resource provides ready-to-use information and activities for remedial students in grades five to eight. Written to grade and using simplified language and vocabulary, **science** concepts are presented in a way that makes them more accessible to students and easier to understand. Comprised of reading passages, student activities and mini posters, our resource can be used effectively for whole-class, small group and independent work.

How Is Our Resource Organized?

STUDENT HANDOUTS

Reading passages and **activities** (*in the form of reproducible worksheets*) make up the majority of our resource. The reading passages present important grade-appropriate information and concepts related to the topic. Embedded in each passage are one or more questions that ensure students understand what they have read.

For each reading passage there are BEFORE YOU READ activities and AFTER YOU READ activities.

- The BEFORE YOU READ activities prepare students for reading by setting a purpose for reading. They stimulate background knowledge and experience, and guide students to make connections between what they know and what they will learn. Important concepts and vocabulary are also presented.

- The AFTER YOU READ activities check students' comprehension of the concepts presented in the reading passage and extend their learning. Students are asked to give thoughtful consideration of the reading passage through creative and evaluative short-answer questions, research, and extension activities.

Hands-on activities are included to further develop students' thinking skills and understanding of the concepts. The **Assessment Rubric** (*page 4*) is a useful tool for evaluating students' responses to many of the activities in our resource. The **Comprehension Quiz** (*page 48*) can be used for either a follow-up review or assessment at the completion of the unit.

PICTURE CUES

This resource contains three main types of pages, each with a different purpose and use. A **Picture Cue** at the top of each page shows, at a glance, what the page is for.

Teacher Guide
- Information and tools for the teacher

Student Handout
- Reproducible worksheets and activities

Easy Marking™ Answer Key
- Answers for student activities

EASY MARKING™ ANSWER KEY

Marking students' worksheets is fast and easy with this **Answer Key**. Answers are listed in columns – just line up the column with its corresponding worksheet, as shown, and see how every question matches up with its answer!

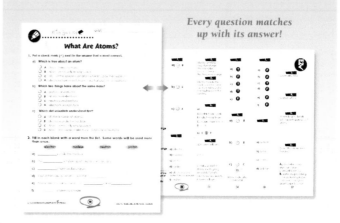

Every question matches up with its answer!

Bloom's Taxonomy

Our resource is an effective tool for any SCIENCE PROGRAM.

Bloom's Taxonomy* for Reading Comprehension

The activities in our resource engage and build the full range of thinking skills that are essential for students' reading comprehension and understanding of important science concepts. Based on the six levels of thinking in Bloom's Taxonomy, and using language at a remedial level, information and questions are given that challenge students to not only recall what they have read, but move beyond this to understand the text and concepts through higher-order thinking. By using higher-order skills of application, analysis, synthesis and evaluation, students become active readers, drawing more meaning from the text, attaining a greater understanding of concepts, and applying and extending their learning in more sophisticated ways.

Our resource, therefore, is an effective tool for any Science program. Whether it is used in whole or in part, or adapted to meet individual student needs, our resource provides teachers with essential information and questions to ask, inspiring students' interest, creativity, and promoting meaningful learning.

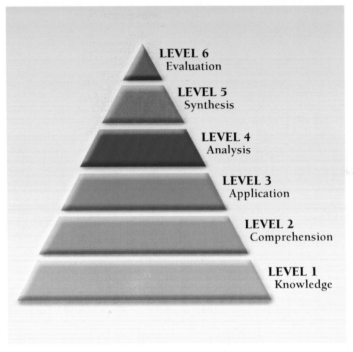

**BLOOM'S TAXONOMY:
6 LEVELS OF THINKING**

Bloom's Taxonomy is a widely used tool by educators for classifying learning objectives, and is based on the work of Benjamin Bloom.

Vocabulary

atom	group	nonmetals
atomic model	inert	organic
atomic number	inert gas	outer electron
bond	metals	particle
chemical symbols	material	periodic table
compound	metal oxide	proton
electron	molecule	pure material
element	neutron	reactive

NAME: _____

 Before You Read

What Are Atoms?

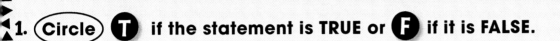

1. **Circle** **T** if the statement is **TRUE** or **F** if it is **FALSE.**

T F **a)** People have always agreed that matter is made of atoms.

T F **b)** Some atoms are large enough to see with our eyes.

T F **c)** All molecules contain more than one atom.

T F **d)** Atoms and molecules are two kinds of particles.

T F **e)** Atoms are made of even smaller parts.

2. **Complete each sentence with a word from the list. Use a dictionary to help you.**

> atom   chemical change   physical change   molecule   particle

a) Melting is a _____.

b) Molecules can break apart into _____s during a chemical change.

c) _____s can form new molecules.

d) All atoms are _____s.

e) Chemical properties tell how and when atoms form _____s.

What Are Atoms?

Matter is made of **atoms.** Atoms are sort of like building blocks or bricks in a building. Like blocks and bricks, some atoms fit together well to make something larger and some don't.

To understand chemical changes, we need to understand what atoms are. Atoms are the smallest bits of matter that get changed around during a chemical change. But, like building blocks, atoms don't change so they will fit better. Think of a child playing with building blocks. She wouldn't saw a block in half to make it fit better.

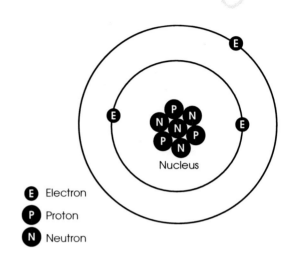

Atomic Model

About 200 years ago, scientists agreed that matter is made of atoms. It took another 100 years to learn what the main parts of atoms are and how they are arranged. This picture shows the three main parts of an atom. They are electrons, protons, and neutrons.

This is called an **atomic model**. A model is not a true picture of a thing. Scientists use models like this to help explain things that are hard to picture exactly. These are some ideas that the atomic model helps us understand:

1. Atoms are mostly empty space.

2. The three main parts of an atom are **electrons**, **protons**, and **neutrons**.

3. Most of the mass of an atom is in the small center area called the **nucleus**. The nucleus is where all the neutrons and protons are found.

4. Electrons circle the nucleus at different distances.

5. Neutrons and protons have about the same mass. Electrons have much less mass than neutrons or protons.

6. The number of electrons in an atom equals the number of protons. The number of neutrons is about the same but can be a little different.

7. Electrons have a minus (or **negative**) electrical charge. Protons have a plus (or **positive**) electrical charge. Neutrons have no charge.

What Are Atoms?

Now let's put all these ideas together: In an atom, small, negative electrons circle the nucleus. The nucleus is made of larger, positive protons and uncharged neutrons. Atoms are mostly empty space. Most of an atom's mass is in the middle. The number of electrons equals number of protons.

Actual atoms

Scientists have learned a lot more than this, but these are the most important things to remember about atoms.

The model on page 8 shows one kind of atom, called a lithium atom. There are about 100 other kinds of atoms, each with its own numbers of electrons, protons, and neutrons.

Suppose the atomic model shown did not have the electrons, protons, and neutrons named. How could you tell which were the PROTONS?

_____

_____

_____

All of these things about atoms were figured out before anyone ever saw an atom. People just thought hard about how matter behaved in experiments. They got ideas, which led to more experiments. After many years, they came up with this model of the atom.

What Are Atoms?

1. Put a check mark (✓) next to the answer that is most correct.

a) Which is true about an atom?

○ **A** Atoms have no mass.
○ **B** Atoms are mostly empty space.
○ **C** Most of the space in an atom is taken up by the nucleus.
○ **D** Electrons have much more mass than protons or neutrons.

b) Which two things have about the same mass?

○ **A** protons and atoms
○ **B** atoms and electrons
○ **C** neutrons and protons
○ **D** electrons and protons

c)   Which did scientists understand first?

○ **A** Matter is made of atoms.
○ **B** Electrons circle the nucleus.
○ **C** Atoms are mostly empty space.
○ **D** Atoms are made of electrons, protons, and neutrons.

2. Fill in each blank with a word from the list. Some words will be used more than once.

electron   nucleus   neutron   proton

a) _____s circle the nucleus.

b) The _____ is made up of neutrons and protons.

c) _____s have a plus charge.

d) Most of the mass of an atom is in the _____.

e) Atoms have the same number of _____s and _____s.

f) _____s have no charge.

What Are Atoms?

3. Tell what kind of **electrical charge** electrons, protons, and neutrons have.

_____

_____

4. Where are electrons, protons, and neutrons found in an atom?

_____

_____

Extensions & Applications

5. On the next page are a table and a diagram about atoms for you to complete.
   a) Show what you have learned about electrons, protons, and neutrons by filling in the table on the next page.
   - **A.** In each box under Mass, write **a lot** or **a little.**
   - **B.** In each box under Charge, write **plus, minus** or **zero.**
   - **C.** In each box under Position, write **inside** or **outside.**
   - **D.** In the last boxes on the right, put a **check mark** in the two boxes for the parts of an atom that have equal mass.
   b) Show what you have learned about electrons, protons, and neutrons by labeling the diagram of the atom on the next page.

6. a) After scientists decided matter is made of atoms, it took about 100 years to figure out the parts of an atom. Why do you think it took so long?

_____

_____

   b) Is an atomic model the same as a real atom?

_____

_____

   c) How is an atomic model useful?

_____

_____

NAME: _____

What Are Atoms?

5. a) Complete the table with information from the reading passage.

Atom Part	A. How much mass? A lot or a little?	B. Electrical Charge plus, minus, or zero?	C. Position inside or outside the nucleus?	D. Which two have about equal mass?
Electron				
Proton				
Neutron				

b) Label the parts of the atom in the diagram below. Write **E** in the circle if it is an ELECTRON. Write **P** in the circle if it is a PROTON. Write **N** in the circle if it is a NEUTRON.

Atomic Model

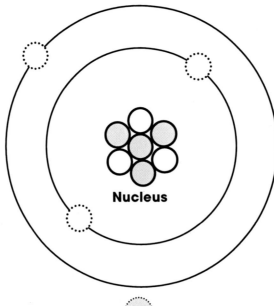

Nucleus

What Are Molecules?

1. **Circle** **T** if the statement is TRUE or **F** if it is FALSE.

T   F   a)   Connecting links between atoms are called **bonds.**

T   F   b)   Atoms contain more than one molecule.

T   F   c)   All particles in a pure material are the same.

T   F   d)   Outer electrons form links that hold atoms together.

T   F   e)   New molecules are formed during physical changes.

2. **Put a check mark (✓) next to the answer that is most correct.**

a) All organic molecules contain the element

○   **A**   calcium
○   **B**   carbon
○   **C**   iron
○   **D**   nitrogen

b) Which is true of all polymer molecules?

○   **A**   They are all gases.
○   **B**   They are all very long.
○   **C**   They can all be used as fuel.
○   **D**   They are all made in factories.

c) Which of these contains one or more bond?

○   **A**   all atoms
○   **B**   all materials
○   **C**   all molecules
○   **D**   all particles

NAME: _____

What Are Molecules?

Silver

Sulfur

Some atoms are separate from each other and other atoms are fastened together. Groups of atoms fastened together are called **molecules**. When atoms fasten together to form molecules it is called a chemical change. When molecules break up into separate atoms, that is a chemical change too.

In molecules, atoms are held together by connecting links. These links are called **bonds**. Atoms become connected when some of the electrons from each atom act together

Silver atoms bond to sulfur atoms to form silver sulfide

to form a bond. Not all electrons can help form bonds. Only the electrons farthest from the nucleus form bonds. Also, not all atoms can bond together. The atoms must have the right number of electrons with the right energy to form a bond. The pictures show what happens when silver atoms bond to sulfur atoms to form silver sulfide.

Complete these sentences by filling the blanks with the words below. Use each word once.

chemical   molecules   atoms

Bonds connect _____ to form _____. A _____ change happens whenever bonds are formed or broken.

Atoms and molecules are two kinds of **particles**. When all the particles in something are the same, it is called a **pure material**. All the particles in pure gold are gold atoms. All the particles in pure water are water molecules.

Scientists often use **chemical symbols** instead of names to talk about atoms. For an atom of oxygen they write "O". For an atom of sulfur they write "S". For some atoms the symbol is a big letter and a little letter. Aluminum is "Al". The symbol can mean just one atom or it can mean a material made of those atoms.

What Are Molecules?

Molecules are made of two or more atoms bonded together. The atoms in a molecule can be different or they can be the same. Oxygen in the air is made of oxygen molecules. An oxygen molecule is two oxygen atoms bonded together. Molecules of water are made of two kinds of atoms. Every water molecule has two hydrogen atoms and one oxygen atom.

Oxygen and water are small molecules. Many of the molecules that make up living things are much larger. Some molecules are made of hundreds or even thousands of atoms! Even these large molecules are much too small to see.

Most molecules in living things are called **organic** molecules. One thing is the same for all organic molecules. They all contain atoms of carbon. Another kind of molecules are called **polymers**. These are very long molecules. Polymer molecules become long by repeating the same small group of atoms over and over. Our clothes are made mostly of polymers. Some of these come from nature, like cotton and wool. Others are made in factories, like nylon and rayon. All these kinds of cloth are made of very long polymer molecules.

NAME: _____

What Are Molecules?

1. **Circle T if the statement is TRUE or F if it is FALSE.**

T F **a)** Water molecules are polymers.

T F **b)** Sodium chloride is an organic molecule.

T F **c)** The letter "O" can mean "one oxygen atom."

T F **d)** A "pure material" can contain many kinds of molecules as long as they are pure.

T F **e)** Chemical bonds between atoms are formed by outer protons.

T F **F)** Any atom can form a molecule with any other atom.

2. **Write each word beside its meaning. Some words will not be used.**

bond	material	molecule
organic	polymer	symbol

_____ **a)** a short way to write the name of an atom

_____ **b)** the connecting link between atoms on a molecule

_____ **c)** a molecule that contains carbon

_____ **d)** a long molecule with repeating groups of atoms

3. **When two atoms bond together to form a molecule, which parts of the atoms become part of the bond?**

_____

_____

What are Molecules?

4. What is part of every *organic* molecule?

_____

_____

5. What kind of molecule is a *polymer*?

_____

_____

Extensions & Applications

6. Learn more about atoms and molecules by studying the materials around you. Some things you often see around you are made of separate atoms. Others are made of molecules. All of the materials listed below are **pure materials**. Some are made of **atoms**, and some are made of **molecules**.

iron	**water**	**oxygen**	**helium**	**neon**	**aluminum**
baking soda	**silver**	**rust**	**charcoal**	**sugar**	

For this activity make a chart like the one below:

A. MADE OF SEPARATE ATOMS		B. MADE OF MOLECULES	
Common Name	Scientific Name	Common Name	Scientific Name

Put each material above in the correct list.
Some of these materials have scientific names. For those that do, write the **scientific name** next to its common name. Looking the names up in a large dictionary will help with some of the materials. Your teacher may also be able to tell you books or websites that will help.
See if you can find any other pure materials to **add** to the list. Try looking in the bathroom, kitchen, classroom, supermarket, and outdoors.

NAME: _____

What Are Elements?

1. (Circle) **T** if the statement is TRUE or **F** if it is FALSE.

T   F   **a)**   There are about 100 different kinds of atoms.

T   F   **b)**   Molecules contain two or more atoms.

T   F   **c)**   Fire, air, earth, and water are all elements.

T   F   **d)**   Forming rust is a chemical property of iron.

T   F   **e)**   All atoms have the same number of electrons.

T   F   **f)**   All atoms are the same size.

2. Draw one line from each word on the left to its meaning.

bonds	**a**	the parts of an atom equal in number to the atom's electrons
chemical	**b**	the properties that tell how and when an atom forms molecules
electrons	**c**	the connections that hold atoms together
elements	**d**	materials made of one kind of atom
protons	**e**	the parts of an atom that circle the nucleus

NAME: _____

What Are Elements?

Atoms of the Two Simplest Elements

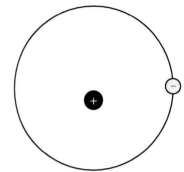

A Hydrogen Atom

You learned earlier that there are about 100 kinds of atoms. A material made of only one kind of atom is called an **element**. Some elements you may know about are iron in nails, helium in balloons, and iodine in medicines.

The atoms of each element have different chemical and physical properties. But why are the atoms different? Atoms of each element have a different number of protons in their nucleus. Hydrogen is the simplest element. Its atoms have only one proton. Uranium has much larger atoms with 92 protons.

Remember that the number of protons in an atom equals the number of electrons. Hydrogen atoms have one electron and uranium atoms have 92 electrons. The number of electrons in the atoms of an element give the element its chemical properties. This is because different numbers of electrons cause atoms to form bonds in different ways.

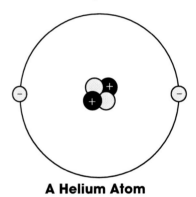

A Helium Atom

Name TWO things that are different about atoms of different elements.

_____

_____

Elements can be made of single atoms, or they can be made of molecules. The helium in helium balloons is made of separate atoms. You may remember that oxygen we breathe is made of molecules that have two oxygen atoms bonded together.

Long ago people thought there were only four elements: fire, air, earth, and water. Now we know that none of these are elements. Water molecules are made of hydrogen and oxygen atoms. The other three are mixtures of different molecules.

NAME: _____

What Are Elements?

1. **Put a check mark (✓) next to the answer that is most correct.**

   a) **How many elements are there?**

   ○ **A** three
   ○ **B** four
   ○ **C** about 100
   ○ **D** many millions

   b) **Why do all atoms of an element have the same chemical properties?**

   ○ **A** They all have the same size electrons.
   ○ **B** Their electrons all have the same charge.
   ○ **C** They all have the same number of neutrons.
   ○ **D** They all have the same number of electrons.

   c) **Long ago, people believed there were four elements: fire, air, earth, and water How many of these are called elements today?**

   ○ **A** none
   ○ **B** one
   ○ **C** two
   ○ **D** three

2. **a)** Circle the words that are the names of elements.

   air   helium   hydrogen   iron   sunlight   water

   b) **Underline the words that are made of elements but are not elements.**

   air   helium   hydrogen   iron   sunlight   water

NAME: _____

What Are Elements?

3. Tell what an *element* is. Use the word "atoms" in your answer.

_____

_____

4. What is the *simplest* element?

_____

_____

5. Name *two* other elements.

_____

_____

Extensions & Applications

6. Look back at the pictures of the atoms of hydrogen and helium. Hydrogen has one proton in its nucleus circled by one electron. Helium has two protons and two neutrons in its nucleus circled by two electrons.

Make drawings of atoms of the elements **carbon** and **lithium**. For both atoms, put the first two electrons in an inner circle and the other electrons in an outer circle.

Carbon has six protons and six neutrons in its nucleus, circled by six electrons.

Lithium has three protons and four neutrons in its nucleus. You will have to figure out how many electrons circle the nucleus of a lithium atom.

NAME: _____

What Are Compounds?

1. Circle T if the statement is TRUE or F if it is FALSE.

T F **a)** Atoms are made of molecules.

T F **b)** Molecules and atoms are particles.

T F **c)** Pure materials are made of one kind of particle.

T F **d)** Atoms can be thought of as the building blocks of matter.

T F **e)** Water is an element.

T F **f)** Electrons are one kind of atom.

2. Put a check mark (✓) next to the answer that is most correct.

a) Which of these is an element?

○ **A** air
○ **B** gold
○ **C** sugar
○ **D** water

b) Which of these is made of more than one atom?

○ **A** a bond
○ **B** a nucleus
○ **C** a molecule
○ **D** an electron

c) There are about 100 different

○ **A** electrons.
○ **B** elements.
○ **C** molecules.
○ **D** particles.

NAME: _____

What Are Compounds?

You have learned that molecules are particles made of more than one atom. If the atoms in the molecules of a material are the same, the material is an element. If the atoms in the molecules of a material are different, the material is a **compound**.

Oxygen   **Salt**   **Sugar**

Remember that atoms and molecules are very small particles. Elements and compounds are materials made of many particles. The particles in a compound are always molecules, not atoms. Because the particles of a molecule have more than one kind of atom, they must have more than one atom. Particles with more than one atom are molecules.

Explain why water is a COMPOUND and not an element.

_____

_____

Remember we learned that all pure materials are made of just one kind of atom or just one kind of molecule. Also pure materials are made of only one element or only one compound.

These are some common elements you may have heard of: hydrogen, helium, carbon, nitrogen, oxygen, neon, aluminum, chlorine, calcium, nickel, copper, silver, iodine, gold, tin, mercury, and lead.

These are some common compounds you may have heard of: salt, sugar, water, rust, and carbon dioxide.

We have been studying four words that are easy to confuse: atoms, molecules, elements, and compounds. This diagram may help you keep them straight. Follow the direction that the arrows point to make sentences. For example, at the top: "**ATOMS** are always **ELEMENTS**." The most important sentences have thick arrows.

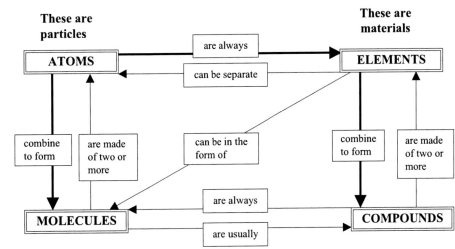

These are particles

These are materials

| ATOMS | are always | ELEMENTS |
| | can be separate | |

combine to form | are made of two or more | can be in the form of | combine to form | are made of two or more

| MOLECULES | are always | COMPOUNDS |
| | are usually | |

NAME: _____

What Are Compounds?

1. Use the words in the list to answer each question.

atoms	molecules	elements
compounds	particles	pure materials

_____ **a)** Which particles make up all elements?

_____ **b)** Which particles are always made of more than one atom?

_____ **c)** What is made of one kind of atom or one kind of molecule?

_____ **d)** Which materials are made of one kind of atom?

_____ **e)** What are single atoms or single molecules called?

_____ **f)** Which materials are made of more than one element?

2. a) (Circle) **the words that are elements.**

aluminum	salt	sugar	oxygen
rust	copper	gold	water

b) <u>Underline</u> **the words that are compounds.**

aluminum	salt	sugar	oxygen
rust	copper	gold	water

NAME: _____

What are Compounds?

3. Tell what elements are using the word "atom."

_____

_____

4. Tell what molecules are using the word "atom."

_____

_____

5. Tell what compounds are using the word "element."

_____

_____

Extensions & Applications

6. Find out what **elements** have combined to form some of the **common compounds** you see around you. You may have to look them up in the dictionary, a science book, or on the Internet. Ask your teacher for the best place to look.

Find the elements that make up these compounds:

a) water

_____

b) glass (It is the same compound as sand.)

_____

c) sugar

_____

d) Try to find **two** more materials you think are compounds. Read about them to see if they really are compounds. If they are compounds, find which elements are in them. See if they have scientific names.

_____

_____

The Periodic Table

1. **Put a check mark (✓) next to the answer that is most correct.**

   a) **What gives the atoms of an element their chemical properties?**

   - ○ **A** the inner protons
   - ○ **B** the outer protons
   - ○ **C** the inner electrons
   - ○ **D** the outer electrons

   b) **What is different for atoms of every element?**

   - ○ **A** the number of electrons
   - ○ **B** the size of the electrons
   - ○ **C** the mass of the electrons
   - ○ **D** the number of outer electrons

   c) **What is a chemical symbol?**

   - ○ **A** the matter at the center of an atom
   - ○ **B** a model showing the parts of an atom
   - ○ **C** the most important property of an element
   - ○ **D** a short way to write the name of an element

2. **Circle T if the statement is TRUE or F if it is FALSE.**

   T F a) Some elements have the same chemical and physical properties.

   T F b) Scientists discovered most of the elements thousands of years ago.

   T F c) Atoms of every element have a different number of protons.

   T F d) All atoms of an element have the same chemical properties.

   T F e) Molecules can be divided into smaller parts called compounds.

26

The Periodic Table

	1														Nonmetals				18
1	**H** 1	2												13	14	15	16	17	**He** 2
2	**Li** 3	**Be** 4												**B** 5	**C** 6	**N** 7	**O** 8	**F** 9	**Ne** 10
3	**Na** 11	**Mg** 12	3	4	5	6	7	8	9	10	11	12		**Al** 13	**Si** 14	**P** 15	**S** 16	**Cl** 17	**Ar** 18
4	**K** 19	**Ca** 20	**Sc** 21	**Ti** 22	**V** 23	**Cr** 24	**Mn** 25	**Fe** 26	**Co** 27	**Ni** 28	**Cu** 29	**Zn** 30	**Ga** 31	**Ge** 32	**As** 33	**Se** 34	**Br** 35	**Kr** 36
5	**Rb** 37	**Sr** 38	**Y** 39	**Zr** 40	**Nb** 41	**Mo** 42	**Tc** 43	**Ru** 44	**Rh** 45	**Pd** 46	**Ag** 47	**Cd** 48	**In** 49	**Sn** 50	**Sb** 51	**Te** 52	**I** 53	**Xe** 54
6	**Cs** 55	**Ba** 56	*	**Hf** 72	**Ta** 73	**W** 74	**Re** 75	**Os** 76	**Ir** 77	**Pt** 78	**Au** 79	**Hg** 80	**Tl** 81	**Pb** 82	**Bi** 83	**Po** 84	**At** 85	**Rn** 86
7	**Fr** 87	**Ra** 88	**	**Rf** 104	**Db** 105	**Sg** 106	**Bh** 107	**Hs** 108	**Mt** 109									

	*	**La** 57	**Ce** 58	**Pr** 59	**Nd** 60	**Pm** 61	**Sm** 62	**Eu** 63	**Gd** 64	**Tb** 65	**Dy** 66	**Ho** 67	**Er** 68	**Tm** 69	**Yb** 70	**Lu** 71
	**	**Ac** 89	**Th** 90	**Pa** 91	**U** 92	**Np** 93	**Pu** 94	**Am** 95	**Cm** 96	**Bk** 97	**Cf** 98	**Es** 99	**Fm** 100	**Md** 101	**No** 102	**Lr** 103

 Each element has its own chemical and physical properties. For hundreds of years, Scientists have tried to learn more about the elements by studying their properties.

Early scientists didn't know much about atoms. They didn't have the atomic model you studied earlier. They did know a little about the mass of atoms. They were able to arrange the elements in order from the atom with least mass to the atom with the most mass.

When they looked at this list, they saw something interesting. The properties of the elements repeated every so often. For example, the 4th, 12th, and 20th elements showed the same properties.

They arranged the elements in a table that showed how properties repeated. Each time the properties started to repeat, they started a new row of the table. This table is called the **periodic table of the elements.** The periodic table shown here is the one scientists use today.

The periodic table told scientists a lot about how each element would behave. It told them when to expect elements to form compounds. But they still didn't understand why elements behaved the way they did. They also did not understand or why properties repeated.

The Periodic Table

I t all became clear when they learned about electrons and protons. Remember that it is the outer electrons that form bonds. Also remember that the way atoms form bonds is what gives an element its chemical properties. So the reason properties repeat is because the number of outer electrons repeats. If atoms of two elements have the same number of outer electrons, they form bonds in the same way.

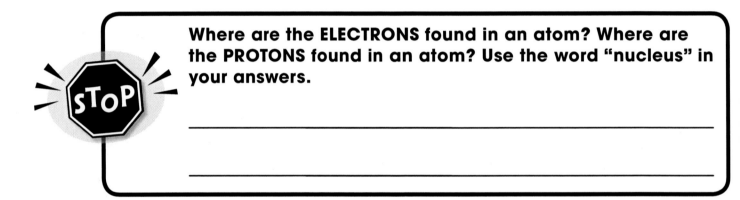

Where are the ELECTRONS found in an atom? Where are the PROTONS found in an atom? Use the word "nucleus" in your answers.

_____

_____

Look at the periodic table. Each square has the symbol of a different element. Some of the symbols do not look like the names of the elements. For example, the symbol for gold is "Au". The numbers in the squares are called **atomic numbers**. Notice that the numbers get bigger from left to right in each row. The atomic number is equal to the number of protons in the nucleus of each atom of that element. The atomic number is also equal to the number of electrons. So each element has one more proton and one more electron than the element just before it.

Each up-and-down row is called a **group**. The groups are numbered from 1 to 18 across the top of the table. Next we will learn what the periodic table shows about properties of the elements.

Sometimes we will put the symbol of an element after its name, so you can find it in the periodic table. For example: hydrogen (H) or helium (He).

NAME: _____

The Periodic Table

1. **Fill in each blank with a word or group of words from the list.**

    atomic number   element   symbol   group   atom

    a) The periodic table lists all the _____s in order of increasing _____s.

    b) The letter "C" is the _____ for the element carbon.

    c) In the periodic table, elements in the same _____ have many of the same properties.

    d) Elements with the smallest _____s are near the top of the periodic table.

2. **Put a check mark (✓) next to the answer that is most correct.**

    a) **What repeats when elements are arranged in order of increasing atomic mass?**

    ○ **A** size of atoms
    ○ **B** atomic numbers
    ○ **C** chemical properties
    ○ **D** number of electrons

    b) **What did scientists study to make the first periodic table?**

    ○ **A** atomic models
    ○ **B** outer electrons
    ○ **C** each atom's nucleus
    ○ **D** properties of elements

The Periodic Table

3. Tell *three* things you can learn about an element by looking at one square in the periodic table.

_____

_____

4. Explain why the scientists who made the first periodic tables didn't understand why properties of elements repeated.

_____

_____

Extensions & Applications

5. A scientist from Russia, named **Dmitri Mendeleev,** made the **first** really good periodic table. Even though he drew up his table about 150 years ago, it is a lot like the one used today. Look for things to read about Mendeleev and his periodic table. Searching for his last name on the Internet will be some help. Your teacher may also have some books to help you.

a) When did he formally present his periodic table?

_____

b) Try to find out what other scientists thought of his periodic table.

_____

_____

_____

c) He left some squares in his table **blank.** Why did he do this? How did this show later that his periodic table was correct?

_____

_____

d) One story says that the periodic table came to Mendeleev in a dream. Try to find out if this story is true.

_____

_____

Patterns In the Periodic Table

1. Circle **T** if the statement is TRUE or **F** if it is FALSE.

T F a) The periodic table came before the atomic model.

T F b) Each element in the periodic table has one more proton than the element to its left.

T F c) Only the most important elements are included in the periodic table.

T F d) The symbol "W" in the periodic table stands for water.

T F e) "Inert" means the same as "reactive."

2. Draw a line from each word or words on the left to its meaning on the right.

inert	**a**	an up-and-down row in the periodic table
bonds	**b**	a material made of one kind of atom
group	**c**	connections between atoms in a molecule
atomic number	**d**	almost never forms compounds with other elements
element	**e**	equal to the number of protons in each atom of an element

Atoms, Molecules & Elements CC4505

NAME: _____

Patterns In the Periodic Table

You learned that the number of electrons increases from left to right in a row of the periodic table. The elements in group 18, at the far right, have a full set of outer electrons. These elements almost never form compounds with anything. We say these elements are **inert**. Since they are all gases, they are called the **inert gases**.

Elements in group 17 are one electron short of a full outer set. They form compounds very easily. This means that they are very **reactive**. The elements in group 1 have just one outer electron, and they are also very reactive.

You wouldn't think that a metal would react with water. But sodium metal (Na) from group 1 reacts with water very quickly. In fact, flames appear when the two materials are put together! Elements in group 1 are most reactive with elements in group 17. Sodium reacts with the element chlorine (Cl) in group 17 to form sodium chloride. Sodium chloride is the scientific name for table salt.

Name an element with ONE outer electron. Name an element with TWO outer electrons. Use the periodic table to help you choose your answers.

_____

_____

Pictures of sodium reacting with water

Patterns
In the Periodic Table

Except for group 18, the most reactive elements are in the groups to the far left and far right. Elements in the top rows are also more reactive than elements in lower rows. So what does it mean when we put these two rules together? We see that the most reactive elements are in the top left and top right parts of the periodic table. When elements from these two parts of the periodic table react with each other, they react very easily and give off a lot of energy.

The periodic table shows other patterns of properties, too. Here is one of the most important things it shows: Elements in each group have very similar properties. For example, as we said, group 18 elements are all gases; these gases are all inert.

The numbers of electrons, protons, and neutrons in atoms all get larger from left to right and from top to bottom. This means the mass of atoms also gets greater in the same directions. So the atoms with the least mass are in the top left of the periodic table. Those atoms with the most mass are in the bottom right.

The size of atoms also gets larger from top to bottom. This is because there are more electrons and they are farther and farther from the nucleus. Changes in size from left to right do not follow a simple rule.

NAME: _____

Patterns In the Periodic Table

Look at the periodic table to help you answer these questions.

1. Number the elements from 1 to 5 in the order of **most** reactive (1) to **least** reactive (5).

<table>
<tr><td>[   ]</td><td>**a)** silver (Ag)</td></tr>
<tr><td>[   ]</td><td>**b)** arsenic (As)</td></tr>
<tr><td>[   ]</td><td>**c)** fluorine (F)</td></tr>
<tr><td>[   ]</td><td>**d)** krypton (Kr)</td></tr>
<tr><td>[   ]</td><td>**e)** nitrogen (N)</td></tr>
</table>

2. **Put a check mark (✓) next to the answer that is most correct.**

   a) Lithium (Li) forms a compound most easily with

   ○ **A** beryllium (Be)
   ○ **B** fluorine (F)
   ○ **C** neon (Ne)
   ○ **D** sodium (Na)

   b) Where are the *most* reactive elements in the periodic table?

   ○ **A** far right row
   ○ **B** top and bottom rows
   ○ **C** lower left and lower right
   ○ **D** upper left and upper right

   c) Which of these elements has properties *most* like those of sodium (Na)?

   ○ **A** argon (Ar)
   ○ **B** chlorine (Cl)
   ○ **C** magnesium (Mg)
   ○ **D** potassium (K)

After You Read

Patterns In the Periodic Table

3. Explain why elements in the same group have many of the same chemical properties.

_____

_____

4. Explain why atoms of elements in the bottom rows of the periodic table are larger than those in the top rows.

_____

_____

Extensions & Applications

Find calcium (Ca), chlorine (Cl), and helium (He) in the periodic table. For each of these elements answer the questions below.

5. Calcium (Ca):

a) Name the two elements with properties most like calcium.

_____

b) How many electrons and protons does an atom of calcium have?

_____

c) Is calcium more reactive than potassium (K)? _____

d) Is a calcium atom larger than a magnesium (Mg) atom? _____

6. Chlorine (Cl):

a) Name the two elements with properties most like chlorine.

_____

b) How many electrons and protons does an atom of chlorine have?

_____

c) Is chlorine more reactive than sulfur (S)? _____

d) Is a chlorine atom larger than a bromine (Br) atom? _____

7. Helium (He):

a) Name the two elements with properties most like helium.

_____

b) How many electrons and protons does an atom of helium have?

_____

c) Is helium more reactive than hydrogen (H)? _____

d) Is a helium atom larger than a neon (Ne) atom? _____

Properties of Important Elements

1. Put a check mark (✓) next to the answer that is most correct.

a) How many protons are in an atom of boron (B)?

○ **A** 2
○ **B** 4
○ **C** 5
○ **D** 13

b) Which word describes both lithium (Li) and fluorine (F)?

○ **A** inert
○ **B** large
○ **C** metallic
○ **D** reactive

c) Which element is in all organic compounds?

○ **A** calcium (Ca)
○ **B** carbon (C)
○ **C** iron (Fe)
○ **D** sodium (Na)

2. (Circle) **T** if the statement is **TRUE** or **F** if it is **FALSE**.

T F   a) Group 18 elements are inert.

T F   b) Group 17 elements are very reactive.

T F   c) Elements in the bottom rows of the periodic table have very small atoms.

T F   d) Hydrogen (H) has the simplest atoms of any element.

T F   e) Most metals react with oxygen.

Properties of Important Elements

Look at the periodic table again. Notice the two black lines. One line zigzags, like steps, and the other is a straight line. These lines separate three important kinds of elements.

Copper   **Silver**   **Gold**

Three Group 11 Metals

The elements to the left of the zigzag line are called **metals**. The elements between the zigzag line and the straight line are called **nonmetals**. You already learned that the elements to the right of the straight line are called inert gases.

Bromine

We said that inert gases almost never react. Metals usually react with nonmetals. This means many compounds are part metal atoms and part nonmetal atoms.

Three Group 17 Nonmetals

Which TWO groups of elements in the periodic table are MOST reactive? Answer by giving the group numbers.

_____

Which group of elements is LEAST reactive?

_____

Many metals react with oxygen (O) to form **metal oxides**. You have probably seen the oxide of iron (Fe). Its common name is rust. Most metals have other properties in common. Many metals are hard and shiny and melt at high temperatures. Some, like gold (Au), silver (Ag), and platinum (Pt), are used to make jewelry. Mercury (Hg) is the only common metal that is a liquid at room temperature.

Many metals can be bent into different shapes without breaking. Heat and electricity pass through most metals easily. Most metals sink in water.

Properties of Important Elements

You already know about a few other metals. Chromium (Cr) is usually called "chrome" and is used on cars. Pennies are made of copper (Cu), and nickels are made of (you guessed it...) nickel (Ni). Lead (Pb) is a heavy, gray metal used to make weights for fishing lines. Tin (Sn) is used to make tin cans, but it is not the whole can. The tin is only a very thin layer on the inside of the can, which is mostly iron.

Most nonmetals have properties opposite those of metals. Most nonmetals aren't shiny, don't bend, and melt at low temperatures. Heat and electricity do not move easily through most nonmetals.

Bromine (Br) is the only nonmetal that is a liquid. Nitrogen (N), oxygen (O), fluorine (F), and chlorine (Cl) are gases, and the others are all solids. Carbon (C) is in almost all of the important compounds that make up plants and animals. Compounds containing carbon are called **organic** compounds. The other elements in organic compounds are mostly nonmetals. Many organic compounds contain hydrogen (H), oxygen (O), nitrogen (N), phosphorus (P), and sulfur (S). Although hydrogen is in group 1, it behaves like a nonmetal in organic compounds.

Carbon takes three interesting forms when it is just an element and not part of a compound. Carbon can be a black lump, as in coal or charcoal. The lead in a lead pencil is not the element lead (Pb); it is a form of carbon, called graphite. Finally, diamonds are a form of the element carbon.

NAME: _____

Properties of Important Elements

1. **What kind of properties do these elements have? Write a word from the list beside each name. Each word will be used twice.**

metal   nonmetal   inert gas

_____ **a)** oxygen (O)

_____ **b)** helium (He)

_____ **c)** carbon (C)

_____ **d)** potassium (K)

_____ **e)** tin (Sn)

_____ **f)** xenon (Xe)

2. **Circle T if the statement is TRUE or F if it is FALSE.**

T   F   **a)**   Most elements are solids at room temperature.

T   F   **b)**   Heat moves easily through metals.

T   F   **c)**   Most nonmetals are shiny and bend easily.

T   F   **d)**   Most metals melt at low temperatures.

T   F   **e)**   Hydrogen (H), oxygen (O), and carbon (C) are in many organic compounds.

Properties of Important Elements

3. In which parts of the periodic table are *metals*, *nonmetals*, and *inert gases* found?

_____

_____

4. Tell *two* ways that metals and nonmetals are different.

_____

_____

_____

Extensions & Applications

5. Look at the periodic table on the next page. You will see that it has some blank squares. Some of the answers to the questions below you will write in these squares.

a) What is the **atomic number** of the missing element between silicon (Si) and sulfur (S)? Write the number in the square.

b) Calcium (Ca) has an atomic number of 20. Write the **symbol** and **atomic number** of calcium in the correct square.

c) Lead (Pb) is a metal in the sixth row. Write the **symbol** for lead in the correct square.

d) Radon (Rn) is an inert gas. Write the **symbol** for radon in the correct square.

e) Carbon is a nonmetal in group 14. Write the **symbol** for carbon in the correct square.

f) Which element has atoms with **13 protons**? _____

g) How many **electrons** are in an atom of radium (Ra)? _____

Properties of Important Elements

1	2		3	4	5	6	7	8	9	10	11	12	13	14	15	16	17	18
																		Nonmetals
H 1																		He 2
Li 3	Be 4												B 5	C 6	N 7	O 8	F 9	Ne 10
Na 11	Mg 12												Al 13	Si 14	P 15	S 16	Cl 17	Ar 18
K 19	Ca 20		Sc 21	Ti 22	V 23	Cr 24	Mn 25	Fe 26	Co 27	Ni 28	Cu 29	Zn 30	Ga 31	Ge 32	As 33	Se 34	Br 35	Kr 36
Rb 37	Sr 38		Y 39	Zr 40	Nb 41	Mo 42	Tc 43	Ru 44	Rh 45	Pd 46	Ag 47	Cd 48	In 49	Sn 50	Sb 51	Te 52	I 53	Xe 54
Cs 55	Ba 56	*		Hf 72	Ta 73	W 74	Re 75	Os 76	Ir 77	Pt 78	Au 79	Hg 80	Tl 81	Pb 82	Bi 83	Po 84	At 85	Rn 86
Fr 87	Ra 88	**		Rf 104	Db 105	Sg 106	Bh 107	Hs 108	Mt 109									

*	La 57	Ce 58	Pr 59	Nd 60	Pm 61	Sm 62	Eu 63	Gd 64	Tb 65	Dy 66	Ho 67	Er 68	Tm 69	Yb 70	Lu 71
**	Ac 89	Th 90	Pa 91	U 92	Np 93	Pu 94	Am 95	Cm 96	Bk 97	Cf 98	Es 99	Fm 100	Md 101	No 102	Lr 103

Atoms, Molecules & Elements CC4505

Atomic Models

For this activity you will DRAW atomic models of these three atoms:

- fluorine (F)
- neon (Ne)
- sodium (Na)

Make them look like the model on page 8. Put two electrons in the first ring and no more than eight in the second. Make a third ring if you need it.

You do not have to draw each neutron in the nucleus. Just use numbers, and write **N** for neutrons and **P** for protons. For example, the nucleus of FLUORINE would look like this:

NEON has 10 neutrons, and SODIUM has 11 neutrons. Use the periodic table to find the number of protons and electrons. Remember to label each atomic model with the correct name.

Compounds and Molecules

On page 14, you saw pictures of the elements silver and sulfur and of the compound silver sulfide.

Try to find more pictures of elements and the compounds they form.

You can usually find a picture of a material on the Internet by searching for its name. Some websites have pictures of all the elements and some have pictures of many compounds. You may be able to find a periodic table that shows a picture of each element in its square.

If you cannot copy and print the pictures, try to **draw** or **describe** the materials. It is interesting when the compound looks very different from the elements they are made of.

Here are some elements and compounds you can look for. You can ask your teacher for other ones.

- **Elements sodium (Na) and chlorine (Cl) form the compound sodium chloride.**

- **Elements silver (Ag) and chlorine (Cl) form the compound silver chloride.**

- **Elements calcium (Ca) and carbon (C) form the compound calcium carbide.**

- **Elements lead (Pb) and sulfur (S) form the compound lead sulfide.**

- **Elements magnesium (Mg) and iodine (I) form the compound magnesium iodide.**

If you can find how the compound is used, tell about it below the pictures. You may find other interesting compounds to look for in books or by asking your teacher.

The Lives of Elements

Choose several elements and see how many interesting FACTS you can find out about them.

Some things you might look for are:

- **When the element was discovered**
- **Why its symbol doesn't sound like its name**
- **What its name means—was it named after a person?**
- **Where on Earth it can be found**
- **What it is used for**
- **What unusual properties it has**

For example, the metal element tungsten has the symbol W because "wolfram" is the German word for tungsten. Tungsten was discovered by Carl Scheele in 1783. Tungsten has the highest melting point of any metal. The glowing wire in the middle of a light bulb is made of tungsten.

You will find interesting facts about most of the elements. You might try **one** element each from groups 1, 17, and 18, and **one or two** of the metals in the middle of the periodic table.

_____

_____

_____

_____

_____

_____

_____

Alchemists

Today, scientists that study elements and compounds are called **CHEMISTS.** Hundreds of years ago they were called **ALCHEMISTS.** They used science, but they were also something like magicians or wizards. They did discover many of the elements and laws of science, but they had some ideas that seem strange today. What they studied was called "alchemy."

Write a short report about the **history of the alchemists**. Find out which elements they discovered. Did they know what elements were? Is the story true that alchemists thought they could change lead into gold?

Use the space below to write notes as you conduct your research.

_____

_____

_____

_____

_____

_____

_____

_____

NAME: _____

Crossword Puzzle!

Across

2. All particles are the same in a ____ material
3. The kind of molecules that contain carbon
6. The smallest bit of an element
8. An element that reacts easily with metals
12. Elements that don't react with anything are ____
13. An up-and-down row in the periodic table
14. A pure material made of more than one element
15. It connects atoms in a molecule

Down

1. A metal and oxygen form a metal ____
2. Found inside the nucleus of an atom
4. Groups 1 and 17 are very _____
5. What you call an atom or a molecule
7. It circles the nucleus
9. Bonds are formed by the ____ electrons
10. An atomic ____ shows how the parts of an atom are arranged
11. It is in the nucleus and has no charge

Word List

Bond	Reactive	Inert
Outer	Oxide	Atom
Pure	Proton	Neutron
Organic	Compound	Model
Particle	Group	Electron
Nonmetal		

NAME: _____

Word Search

Find all of the words in the Word Search. Words are written horizontally, vertically, diagonally, and some are even written backwards.

B	O	C	P	E	R	I	O	D	I	C
D	X	F	G	H	P	J	N	K	L	W
R	I	T	Y	U	R	U	P	S	D	L
E	D	K	R	J	O	H	O	G	F	A
L	E	E	L	P	T	E	Z	R	X	I
C	S	Y	M	B	O	L	S	A	G	R
I	N	O	O	O	N	E	B	V	C	E
T	C	M	T	N	L	M	R	W	L	T
R	L	P	A	D	Y	E	T	E	R	A
A	E	K	J	H	B	N	C	G	F	M
P	V	T	C	M	X	T	Z	U	S	D
B	N	M	U	T	R	E	N	I	L	Q
Y	T	N	M	O	D	E	L	R	W	E
P	S	D	N	E	U	T	R	O	N	F

ATOM	INERT	PERIODIC
BOND	MATERIAL	PROTON
COMPOUND	MOLECULE	SYMBOLS
ELECTRON	NUMBER	NEUTRON
ELEMENT	OUTER	MODEL
GAS	OXIDE	
GROUP	PARTICLE	

NAME: _____

Comprehension Quiz

25

Part A

This is a model of a beryllium atom.
Label each part of the atom. Tell the name, charge, and mass of the part. For charge, write **minus**, **plus**, or **zero**. For mass, write **not much** or **a lot**.

1. Name _____

2. Charge _____

3. Mass _____

3

1. Name _____

2. Charge _____

3. Mass _____

3

1. Name _____

2. Charge _____

3. Mass _____

3

SUBTOTAL: /9

📖 Reading Passage
• • • • • • • • • • • • • • • • • • •
Comprehension Quiz

Part B

Answer each question in complete sentences.

1. Use the word "particle" to explain what a **pure material** is. Name the **two** kinds of particles. ⟨3⟩

_____

_____

_____

2. Use the words "atom" and "material" to explain what an **element** is. ⟨3⟩

_____

_____

_____

3. Use the words "element" and "material" to explain what a **compound** is. ⟨3⟩

_____

_____

_____

4. Tell how the elements in a "group" in the periodic table are arranged. Use the word "electrons" to explain why elements in a group have the same kind of properties. Where are the elements with the smallest atoms found in a group? ⟨4⟩

_____

_____

_____

5. Where are the **metals**, **nonmetals**, and **inert gases** found in the periodic table? ⟨3⟩

_____

_____

_____

SUBTOTAL: /16

4. Carbon atoms

5. A very long molecule with repeating groups of atoms

6. (Scientific names are in brackets)

A. iron, helium, neon, aluminum, silver, charcoal (carbon)

B. water, oxygen, baking soda (sodium hydrogen carbonate), rust (iron oxide) sugar (sucrose)

17

1.
a) F
b) F
c) T
d) F
e) F
f) F

2.
a) symbol
b) bond
c) organic
d) polymer

3. Outer electrons

16

1.
a) T
b) F
c) T
d) T
e) F

2.
a) ✓ B
b) ✓ B
c) ✓ C

13

atoms, molecules, chemical

14

---

3. Electrons – minus/ negative charge
Protons – plus/ positive charge
Neutrons – no charge

4. Electrons circle the nucleus, protons and neutrons are found in the nucleus (or in the center).

5. a)
A. E – a little, P – a lot, N – a lot
B. E – minus, P – plus, N – zero
C. E – outside, P – inside, N – inside
D. P – ✓, N – ✓

b) E P N

6. a) Answers will vary

b) No

c) Helps us explain what atoms are by giving a model of what is hard to picture exactly. Answers will vary.

11

1.
a) ✓ B
b) ✓ C
c) ✓ A

2.
a) electron
b) nucleus
c) proton
d) nucleus
e) electron, proton (order may be reversed)
f) neutron

10

1.
a) F
b) F
c) T
d) T
e) T

2.
a) physical change
b) atom
c) chemical change
d) particle
e) molecule

7

The number of protons equals the number of electrons. Answers will vary.

9

3. Elements contain one kind of atom.

4. Molecules contain more than one atom.

5. Compounds are made of more than one element.

6.
a) hydrogen, oxygen
b) silicon, oxygen
c) carbon, hydrogen, oxygen
d) Accept any verifiable answer

(25)

1.
a) atoms
b) molecules
c) pure materials
d) elements
e) particles
f) compounds

2.
a) (aluminum) (copper) (gold) (oxygen)
b) salt   sugar   rust   water

(24)

1.
a) F
b) T
c) T
d) T
e) F
f) F

2.
a) B
b) C
c) B

(22)

Accept one of:
Water molecules contain more than one kind of atom.
OR
Water is made of more than one element.

(23)

---

3. A material made of one kind of atom

4. Hydrogen has the simplest atoms

5. Answers will vary

6.
Lithium atom
Carbon atom

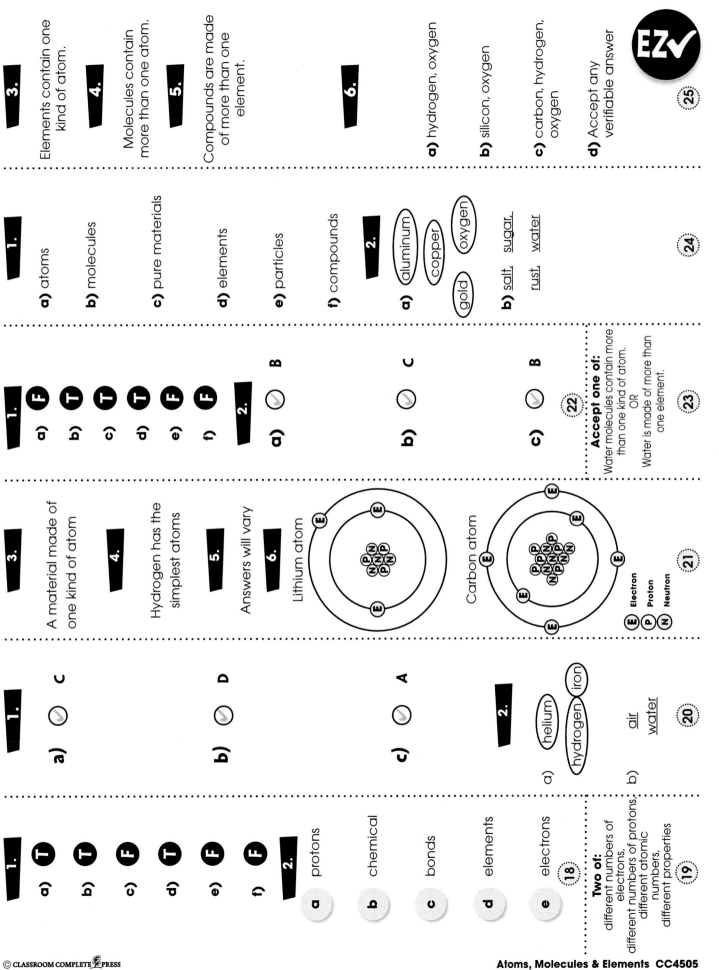

E Electron
P Proton
N Neutron

(21)

1.
a) C
b) D
c) A

2.
a) (helium) hydrogen (iron)
b) air   water

(20)

1.
a) T
b) T
c) F
d) T
e) F
f) F

2.
a protons
b chemical
c bonds
d elements
e electrons

(18)

Two of:
different numbers of electrons, different numbers of protons, different atomic numbers, different properties

(19)

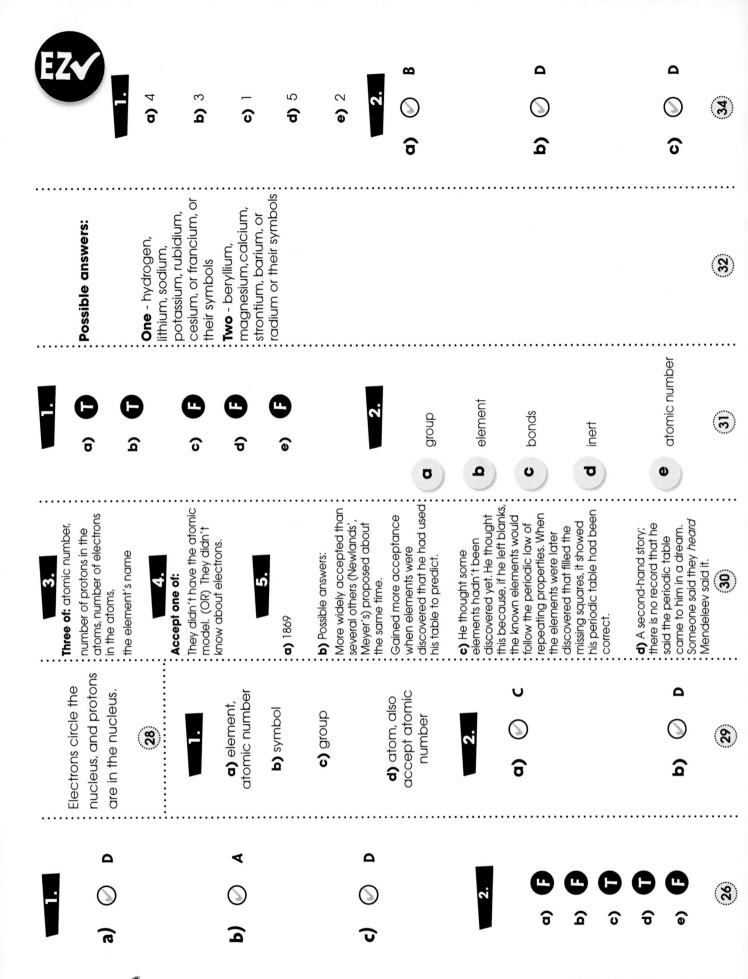

EZ✓

1.
a) 4
b) 3
c) 1
d) 5
e) 2

2.
a) B
b) D
c) D

(34)

Possible answers:

One - hydrogen, lithium, sodium, potassium, rubidium, cesium, or francium, or their symbols

Two - beryllium, magnesium, calcium, strontium, barium, or radium or their symbols

(32)

1.
a) T
b) T
c) F
d) F
e) F

2.
a group
b element
c bonds
d inert
e atomic number

(31)

---

3. Three of: atomic number, number of protons in the atoms, number of electrons in the atoms, the element's name

4. Accept one of: They didn't have the atomic model. (OR) They didn't know about electrons.

5.
a) 1869

b) Possible answers:
More widely accepted than several others (Newlands', Meyer's) proposed about the same time.

Gained more acceptance when elements were discovered that he had used his table to predict.

c) He thought some elements hadn't been discovered yet. He thought this because, if he left blanks, the known elements would follow the periodic law of repeating properties. When the elements were later discovered that filled the missing squares, it showed his periodic table had been correct.

d) A second-hand story; there is no record that he said the periodic table came to him in a dream. Someone said they *heard* Mendeleev said it.

(30)

Electrons circle the nucleus, and protons are in the nucleus.

(28)

1.
a) element, atomic number
b) symbol
c) group
d) atom, also accept atomic number

2.
a) C
b) D

(29)

1.
a) D
b) A
c) D

2.
a) F
b) F
c) T
d) T
e) F

(26)

Fluorine:

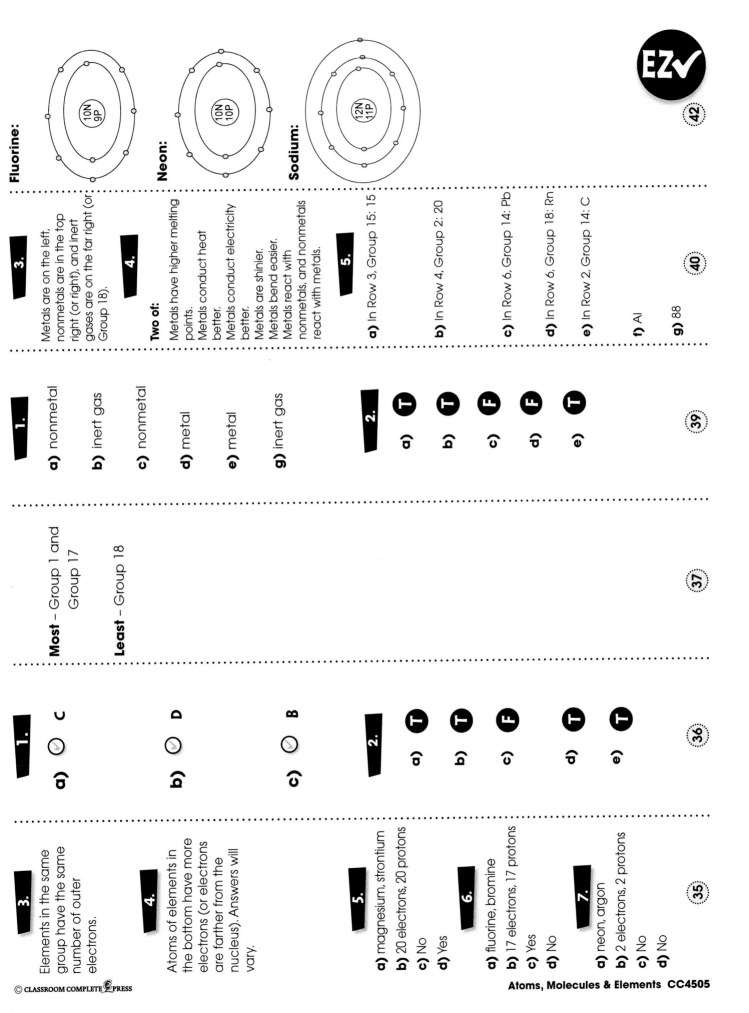

(10N 9P)

Neon:

(10N 10P)

Sodium:

(12N 11P)

3.

Metals are on the left, nonmetals are in the top right (or right), and inert gases are on the far right (or Group 18).

4.

Two of:

Metals have higher melting points.
Metals conduct heat better.
Metals conduct electricity better.
Metals are shinier.
Metals bend easier.
Metals react with nonmetals, and nonmetals react with metals.

5.

a) In Row 3, Group 15: 15

b) In Row 4, Group 2: 20

c) In Row 6, Group 14: Pb

d) In Row 6, Group 18: Rn

e) In Row 2, Group 14: C

f) Al

g) 88

1.

a) nonmetal

b) inert gas

c) nonmetal

d) metal

e) metal

g) inert gas

2.

a) T

b) T

c) F

d) F

e) T

Most – Group 1 and Group 17

Least – Group 18

1.

a) ○ C

b) ○ D

c) ○ B

2.

a) T

b) T

c) F

d) T

e) T

3.

Elements in the same group have the same number of outer electrons.

4.

Atoms of elements in the bottom have more electrons (or electrons are farther from the nucleus). Answers will vary.

5.

a) magnesium, strontium

b) 20 electrons, 20 protons

c) No

d) Yes

6.

a) fluorine, bromine

b) 17 electrons, 17 protons

c) Yes

d) No

7.

a) neon, argon

b) 2 electrons, 2 protons

c) No

d) No

Atoms, Molecules & Elements CC4505

Word Search Answers

Part B

1. A pure material is something made of one kind of particle. The two kinds of particles are atoms and molecules.

2. An element is a material made of one kind of atom.

3. A compound is a material made of two or more elements.

4. Elements in a group are arranged in an up-and-down row (or vertically). Elements in a group have the same properties because they have the same number of outer electrons. Elements with the smallest atoms are at the top of groups.

5. Metals are on the left, nonmetals are in the top right (or right), and inert gases are on the far right (or Group 18).

Part A

1. electron
2. minus
3. not much

1. neutron
2. zero
3. a lot

1. proton
2. plus
3. a lot

Across:

2. pure
3. organic
6. atom
8. nonmetal
12. inert
13. group
14. compound
15. bond

Down:

1. oxide
2. proton
4. reactive
5. particle
7. electron
9. outer
10. model
11. neutron

B	O	C	P	E	R	I	O	D	I	C
D	X	F	G	H	U	J	N	K	L	W
R	I	T	Y	U	I	P	O	S	D	L
E	D	K	R	J	R	H	G	F	A
L	E	E	L	P	T	E	Z	R	X	I
C	S	Y	M	O	O	L	S	A	G	R
	I	N	O	T	N	N	E	B	V	C	E
T	C	M	L	Y	M	W	L	T
A	E	K	J	H	B	Y	E	R	A
P	V	T	C	M	X	T	N	G	F	M
B	N	M	U	T	R	E	N	I	L	D
Y	T	N	M	O	D	E	L	R	Q
P	S	D	N	E	U	T	R	O	N	E
										F

Atoms, Molecules & Elements CC4505

Atomic Models

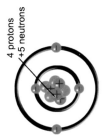

4 protons
+5 neutrons

Beryllium

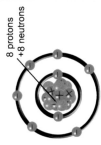

8 protons
+8 neutrons

Oxygen

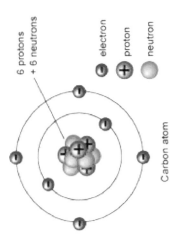

6 protons
+ 6 neutrons

electron
proton
neutron

Carbon atom

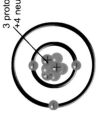

3 protons
+4 neutrons

Lithium

7 protons
+7 neutrons

Nitrogen

2 protons
+2 neutrons

Helium

6 protons
+6 neutrons

Carbon

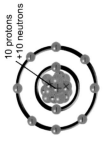

10 protons
+10 neutrons

Neon

+1 neutrons

Hydrogen

5 protons
+6 neutrons

Boron

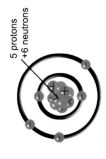

9 protons
+10 neutrons

Fluorine

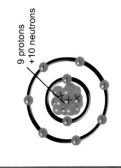

Atoms, Molecules & Elements CC4505

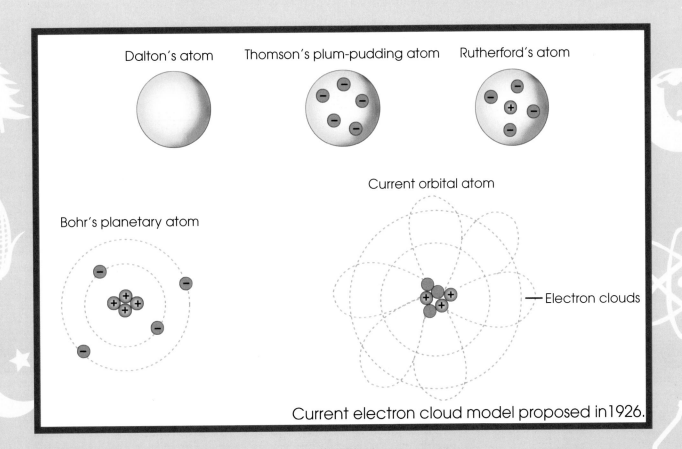

Dalton's atom

Thomson's plum-pudding atom

Rutherford's atom

Current orbital atom

Bohr's planetary atom

Electron clouds

Current electron cloud model proposed in 1926.

Dalton
1803

Thompson
1897

Rutherford
1909

Bohr
1913

Elements and Compounds

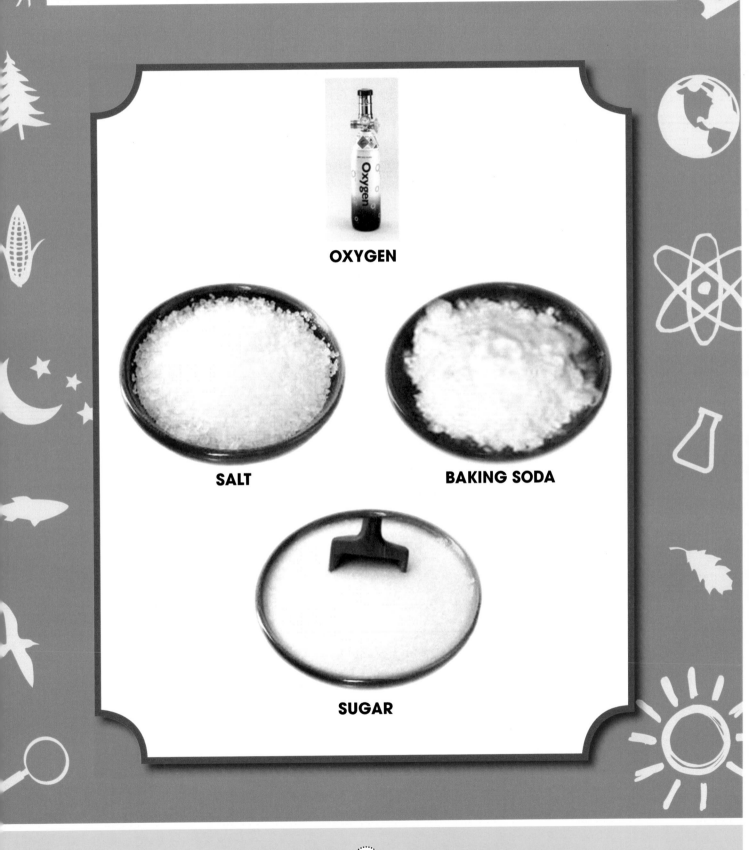

OXYGEN

SALT

BAKING SODA

SUGAR

Group / Period	I	II	III	IV	V	VI	VII	VIII
1	H=1							
2	Li=7	Be=9.4	B=11	C=12	N=14	O=16	F=19	
3	Na=23	Mg=24	Al=27.3	Si=28	P=31	S=32	Cl=35.5	
4	K=39	Ca=40	?=44	Ti=48	V=51	Cr=52	Mn=55	Fe=56, Co=59 Ni=59
5	Cu=63	Zn=65	?=68	?=72	As=75	Se=78	Br=80	
6	Rb=85	Sr=87	?Yt=88	Zr=90	Nb=94	Mo=96	?=100	Ru=104, Rh=104 Pd=106
7	Ag=108	Cd=112	In=113	Sn=118	Sb=122	Te=125	J=127	
8	Cs=133	Ba=137	?Di=138	?Ce=140				
9								
10			?Er=178	?La=180	Ta=182	W=184		O=195, h=197 Pt=198
11	Au=199	Hg=200	Tl=204	Pb=207	Bi=208			
12				Th=231		U=240		

Mendeleev

Mendeleev's Periodic Table

Atoms, Molecules & Elements CC4505

Publication Listing

SOCIAL STUDIES - Books

ITEM #	TITLE
	DAILY LIFE SKILLS SERIES
CC5790	Daily Marketplace Skills Gr. 6-12
CC5791	Daily Social & Workplace Skills Gr. 6-12
CC5792	Daily Health & Hygiene Skills Gr. 6-12
CC5793	Daily Life Skills Big Book Gr. 6-12
	21ST CENTURY SKILLS SERIES
CC5794	Learning Problem Solving Gr. 3-8
CC5795	Learning Communication & Teamwork Gr. 3-8
CC5796	Learning Skills for Global Competency Gr. 3-8
CC5797	Learning to Learn Big Book Gr. 3-8
	MAPPING SKILLS SERIES
CC5786	Gr. PK-2 Mapping Skills with Google Earth
CC5787	Gr. 3-5 Mapping Skills with Google Earth
CC5788	Gr. 6-8 Mapping Skills with Google Earth
CC5789	Gr. PK-8 Mapping Skills with Google Earth Big Book
	NORTH AMERICAN GOVERNMENTS SERIES
CC5757	American Government Gr. 5-8
CC5758	Canadian Government Gr. 5-8
CC5759	Mexican Government Gr. 5-8
CC5760	Governments of North America Big Book Gr. 5-8
	WORLD GOVERNMENTS SERIES
CC5761	World Political Leaders Gr. 5-8
CC5762	World Electoral Processes Gr. 5-8
CC5763	Capitalism vs. Communism Gr. 5-8
CC5777	World Politics Big Book Gr. 5-8
	WORLD CONFLICT SERIES
CC5511	American Revolutionary War Gr. 5-8
CC5500	American Civil War Gr. 5-8
CC5512	American Wars Big Book Gr. 5-8
CC5501	World War I Gr. 5-8
CC5502	World War II Gr. 5-8
CC5503	World Wars I & II Big Book Gr. 5-8
CC5505	Korean War Gr. 5-8
CC5506	Vietnam War Gr. 5-8
CC5507	Korean & Vietnam Wars Big Book Gr. 5-8
CC5508	Persian Gulf War (1990-1991) Gr. 5-8
CC5509	Iraq War (2003-2010) Gr. 5-8
CC5510	Gulf Wars Big Book Gr. 5-8
	WORLD CONTINENTS SERIES
CC5750	North America Gr. 5-8
CC5751	South America Gr. 5-8
CC5768	The Americas Big Book Gr. 5-8
CC5752	Europe Gr. 5-8
CC5753	Africa Gr. 5-8
CC5754	Asia Gr. 5-8
CC5755	Australia Gr. 5-8
CC5756	Antarctica Gr. 5-8
	WORLD CONNECTIONS SERIES
CC5782	Culture, Society & Globalization Gr. 5-8
CC5783	Economy & Globalization Gr. 5-8
CC5784	Technology & Globalization Gr. 5-8
CC5785	Globalization Big Book Gr. 5-8

SOCIAL STUDIES - Software

ITEM #	TITLE
	MAPPING SKILLS SERIES
CC7770	Gr. PK-2 Mapping Skills with Google Earth
CC7771	Gr. 3-5 Mapping Skills with Google Earth
CC7772	Gr. 6-8 Mapping Skills with Google Earth
CC7773	Gr. PK-8 Mapping Skills with Google Earth Big Box

SCIENCE - Software

ITEM #	TITLE
	SPACE AND BEYOND SERIES
CC7557	Solar System Gr. 5-8
CC7558	Galaxies & the Universe Gr. 5-8
CC7559	Travel & Technology Gr. 5-8
CC7560	Space Big Box Gr. 5-8
	HUMAN BODY SERIES
CC7549	Cells, Skeletal & Muscular Systems Gr. 5-8
CC7550	Senses, Nervous & Respiratory Systems Gr. 5-8
CC7551	Circulatory, Digestive & Reproductive Systems Gr. 5-8
CC7552	Human Body Big Box Gr. 5-8
	FORCE, MOTION & SIMPLE MACHINES SERIES
CC7553	Force Gr. 3-8
CC7554	Motion Gr. 3-8
CC7555	Simple Machines Gr. 3-8
CC7556	Force, Motion & Simple Machines Big Box Gr. 3-8

ENVIRONMENTAL STUDIES - Software

ITEM #	TITLE
	CLIMATE CHANGE SERIES
CC7747	Global Warming: Causes Gr. 3-8
CC7748	Global Warming: Effects Gr. 3-8
CC7749	Global Warming: Reduction Gr. 3-8
CC7750	Global Warming Big Box Gr. 3-8

LANGUAGE ARTS - Software

ITEM #	TITLE
CC7112	Word Families - Short Vowels Gr. PK-2
CC7113	Word Families - Long Vowels Gr. PK-2
CC7114	Word Families - Vowels Big Box Gr. PK-2
CC7100	High Frequency Sight Words Gr. PK-2
CC7101	High Frequency Picture Words Gr. PK-2
CC7102	Sight & Picture Words Big Box Gr. PK-2
CC7104	How to Write a Paragraph Gr. 3-8
CC7105	How to Write a Book Report Gr. 3-8
CC7106	How to Write an Essay Gr. 3-8
CC7107	Master Writing Big Box Gr. 3-8
CC7108	Reading Comprehension Gr. 5-8
CC7109	Literary Devices Gr. 5-8
CC7110	Critical Thinking Gr. 5-8
CC7111	Master Reading Big Box Gr. 5-8

MATHEMATICS - Software

ITEM #	TITLE
	PRINCIPLES & STANDARDS OF MATH SERIES
CC7315	Gr. PK-2 Five Strands of Math Big Box
CC7316	Gr. 3-5 Five Strands of Math Big Box
CC7317	Gr. 6-8 Five Strands of Math Big Box

SCIENCE - Books

ITEM #	TITLE
	HANDS-ON STEAM SCIENCE SERIES
CC4100	Physical Science Gr. 1-5
CC4101	Life Science Gr. 1-5
CC4102	Earth & Space Science Gr. 1-5
CC4103	Hands-On Science Big Book Gr. 1-5
	ECOLOGY & THE ENVIRONMENT SERIES
CC4500	Ecosystems Gr. 5-8
CC4501	Classification & Adaptation Gr. 5-8
CC4502	Cells Gr. 5-8
CC4503	Ecology & The Environment Big Book Gr. 5-8
	MATTER & ENERGY SERIES
CC4504	Properties of Matter Gr. 5-8
CC4505	Atoms, Molecules & Elements Gr. 5-8
CC4506	Energy Gr. 5-8
CC4507	The Nature of Matter Big Book Gr. 5-8
	FORCE & MOTION SERIES
CC4508	Force Gr. 5-8
CC4509	Motion Gr. 5-8
CC4510	Simple Machines Gr. 5-8
CC4511	Force, Motion & Simple Machines Big Book Gr. 5-8
	SPACE & BEYOND SERIES
CC4512	Solar System Gr. 5-8
CC4513	Galaxies & The Universe Gr. 5-8
CC4514	Travel & Technology Gr. 5-8
CC4515	Space Big Book Gr. 5-8
	HUMAN BODY SERIES
CC4516	Cells, Skeletal & Muscular Systems Gr. 5-8
CC4517	Senses, Nervous & Respiratory Systems Gr. 5-8
CC4518	Circulatory, Digestive & Reproductive Systems Gr. 5-8
CC4519	Human Body Big Book Gr. 5-8

ENVIRONMENTAL STUDIES - Books

ITEM #	TITLE
	MANAGING OUR WASTE SERIES
CC5764	Waste: At the Source Gr. 5-8
CC5765	Prevention, Recycling & Conservation Gr. 5-8
CC5766	Waste: The Global View Gr. 5-8
CC5767	Waste Management Big Book Gr. 5-8
	CLIMATE CHANGE SERIES
CC5769	Global Warming: Causes Gr. 5-8
CC5770	Global Warming: Effects Gr. 5-8
CC5771	Global Warming: Reduction Gr. 5-8
CC5772	Global Warming Big Book Gr. 5-8
	GLOBAL WATER SERIES
CC5773	Conservation: Fresh Water Resources Gr. 5-8
CC5774	Conservation: Ocean Water Resources Gr. 5-8
CC5775	Conservation: Waterway Habitat Resources Gr. 5-8
CC5776	Water Conservation Big Book Gr. 5-8
	CARBON FOOTPRINT SERIES
CC5778	Reducing Your Own Carbon Footprint Gr. 5-8
CC5779	Reducing Your School's Carbon Footprint Gr. 5-8
CC5780	Reducing Your Community's Carbon Footprint Gr. 5-8
CC5781	Carbon Footprint Big Book Gr. 5-8

LITERATURE KITS™ - Novel Study Guides

ITEM #	TITLE
	GRADES 1-2
CC2100	Curious George (H. A. Rey)
CC2101	Paper Bag Princess (Robert N. Munsch)
CC2102	Stone Soup (Marcia Brown)
CC2103	The Very Hungry Caterpillar (Eric Carle)
CC2104	Where the Wild Things Are (Maurice Sendak)
CC2105	The One in the Middle is the Green Kangaroo (Judy Bloom)
	GRADES 3-4
CC2300	Babe: The Gallant Pig (Dick King-Smith)
CC2301	Because of Winn-Dixie (Kate DiCamillo)
CC2302	The Tale of Despereaux (Kate DiCamillo)
CC2303	James and the Giant Peach (Roald Dahl)
CC2304	Ramona Quimby, Age 8 (Beverly Cleary)
CC2305	The Mouse and the Motorcycle (Beverly Cleary)
CC2306	Charlotte's Web (E.B. White)
CC2307	Owls in the Family (Farley Mowat)
CC2308	Sarah, Plain and Tall (Patricia MacLachlan)
CC2309	Matilda (Roald Dahl)
CC2310	Charlie & The Chocolate Factory (Roald Dahl)
CC2311	Frindle (Andrew Clements)
CC2312	M.C. Higgins, the Great (Virginia Hamilton)
CC2313	The Family Under The Bridge (N.S. Carlson)
CC2314	The Hundred Penny Box (Sharon Mathis)
CC2315	Cricket in Times Square (George Selden)
CC2316	Fantastic Mr Fox (Roald Dahl)
CC2317	The Hundred Dresses (Eleanor Estes)
CC2318	The War with Grandpa (Robert Kimmel Smith)
CC2319	Chocolate Fever (Robert Kimmel Smith)
CC2320	The Chocolate Touch (Patrick Skene Catling)
CC2321	The BFG (Roald Dahl)
	GRADES 5-6
CC2500	Black Beauty (Anna Sewell)
CC2501	Bridge to Terabithia (Katherine Paterson)
CC2502	Bud, Not Buddy (Christopher Paul Curtis)
CC2503	The Egypt Game (Zilpha Keatley Snyder)
CC2504	The Great Gilly Hopkins (Katherine Paterson)
CC2505	Holes (Louis Sachar)
CC2506	Number the Stars (Lois Lowry)
CC2507	The Sign of the Beaver (E.G. Speare)
CC2508	The Whipping Boy (Sid Fleischman)
CC2509	Island of the Blue Dolphins (Scott O'Dell)
CC2510	Underground to Canada (Barbara Smucker)
CC2511	Loser (Jerry Spinelli)
CC2512	The Higher Power of Lucky (Susan Patron)
CC2513	Kira-Kira (Cynthia Kadohata)
CC2514	Dear Mr. Henshaw (Beverly Cleary)
CC2515	The Summer of the Swans (Betsy Byars)
CC2516	Shiloh (Phyllis Reynolds Naylor)
CC2517	A Single Shard (Linda Sue Park)
CC2518	Hoot (Carl Hiaasen)
CC2519	Hatchet (Gary Paulsen)
CC2520	The Giver (Lois Lowry)
CC2521	The Graveyard Book (Neil Gaiman)
CC2522	The View From Saturday (E.L. Konigsburg)
CC2523	Hattie Big Sky (Kirby Larson)
CC2524	When You Reach Me (Rebecca Stead)
CC2525	Criss Cross (Lynne Rae Perkins)
CC2526	A Year Down Yonder (Richard Peck)
CC2527	Maniac Magee (Jerry Spinelli)
CC2528	From the Mixed-Up Files of Mrs. Basil E. Frankweiler (E.L. Konigsburg)

LITERATURE KITS™ - Novel Study Guides

ITEM #	TITLE
CC2529	Sing Down the Moon (Scott O'Dell)
CC2530	The Phantom Tollbooth (Norton Juster)
CC2531	Gregor the Overlander (Suzanne Collins)
CC2532	Through the Looking-Glass (Lewis Carroll)
CC2533	Wonder (R.J. Palacio)
CC2534	Freak the Mighty (Rodman Philbrick)
CC2535	Tuck Everlasting (Natalie Babbitt)
CC2536	My Side of the Mountain (Jean Craighead George)
CC2537	Esperanza Rising (Pam Muñoz Ryan)
	GRADES 7-8
CC2700	Cheaper by the Dozen (Frank B. Gilbreth)
CC2701	The Miracle Worker (William Gibson)
CC2702	The Red Pony (John Steinbeck)
CC2703	Treasure Island (Robert Louis Stevenson)
CC2704	Romeo & Juliet (William Shakespeare)
CC2705	Crispin: The Cross of Lead (Avi)
CC2706	Call It Courage (Armstrong Sperry)
CC2707	The Boy in the Striped Pajamas (John Boyne)
CC2708	The Westing Game (Ellen Raskin)
CC2709	The Cay (Theodore Taylor)
CC2710	The Hunger Games (Suzanne Collins)
CC2711	Catching Fire (Suzanne Collins)
CC2712	The Pearl (John Steinbeck)
	GRADES 9-12
CC2001	To Kill A Mockingbird (Harper Lee)
CC2002	Angela's Ashes (Frank McCourt)
CC2003	The Grapes of Wrath (John Steinbeck)
CC2004	The Good Earth (Pearl S. Buck)
CC2005	The Road (Cormac McCarthy)
CC2006	The Old Man and the Sea (Ernest Hemingway)
CC2007	Lord of the Flies (William Golding)
CC2008	The Color Purple (Alice Walker)
CC2009	The Outsiders (S.E. Hinton)
CC2010	Hamlet (William Shakespeare)
CC2011	The Great Gatsby (F. Scott Fitzgerald)
CC2012	The Adventures of Huckleberry Finn (Mark Twain)
CC2013	Macbeth (William Shakespeare)
CC2014	Fahrenheit 451 (Ray Bradbury)
CC2015	The Crucible (Arthur Miller)
CC2016	Of Mice and Men (John Steinbeck)
CC2017	Divergent (Veronica Roth)

LANGUAGE ARTS - Books

ITEM #	TITLE
CC1110	Word Families - Short Vowels Gr. K-1
CC1111	Word Families - Long Vowels Gr. K-1
CC1112	Word Families - Vowels Big Book Gr. K-1
CC1113	High Frequency Sight Words Gr. K-1
CC1114	High Frequency Picture Words Gr. K-1
CC1115	Sight & Picture Words Big Book Gr. K-1
CC1100	How to Write a Paragraph Gr. 5-8
CC1101	How to Write a Book Report Gr. 5-8
CC1102	How to Write an Essay Gr. 5-8
CC1103	Master Writing Big Book Gr. 5-8
CC1116	Reading Comprehension Gr. 5-8
CC1117	Literary Devices Gr. 5-8
CC1118	Critical Thinking Gr. 5-8
CC1119	Master Reading Big Book Gr. 5-8
CC1106	Reading Response Forms: Gr. 1-2
CC1107	Reading Response Forms: Gr. 3-4
CC1108	Reading Response Forms: Gr. 5-6
CC1109	Reading Response Forms Big Book: Gr. 1-6

MATHEMATICS - Books

ITEM #	TITLE
	TASK SHEETS
CC3100	Gr. PK-2 Number & Operations Task Sheets
CC3101	Gr. PK-2 Algebra Task Sheets
CC3102	Gr. PK-2 Geometry Task Sheets
CC3103	Gr. PK-2 Measurement Task Sheets
CC3104	Gr. PK-2 Data Analysis & Probability Task Sheets
CC3105	Gr. PK-2 Five Strands of Math Big Book Task Sheets
CC3106	Gr. 3-5 Number & Operations Task Sheets
CC3107	Gr. 3-5 Algebra Task Sheets
CC3108	Gr. 3-5 Geometry Task Sheets
CC3109	Gr. 3-5 Measurement Task Sheets
CC3110	Gr. 3-5 Data Analysis & Probability Task Sheets
CC3111	Gr. 3-5 Five Strands of Math Big Book Task Sheets
CC3112	Gr. 6-8 Number & Operations Task Sheets
CC3113	Gr. 6-8 Algebra Task Sheets
CC3114	Gr. 6-8 Geometry Task Sheets
CC3115	Gr. 6-8 Measurement Task Sheets
CC3116	Gr. 6-8 Data Analysis & Probability Task Sheets
CC3117	Gr. 6-8 Five Strands of Math Big Book Task Sheets
	DRILL SHEETS
CC3200	Gr. PK-2 Number & Operations Drill Sheets
CC3201	Gr. PK-2 Algebra Drill Sheets
CC3202	Gr. PK-2 Geometry Drill Sheets
CC3203	Gr. PK-2 Measurement Drill Sheets
CC3204	Gr. PK-2 Data Analysis & Probability Drill Sheets
CC3205	Gr. PK-2 Five Strands of Math Big Book Drill Sheets
CC3206	Gr. 3-5 Number & Operations Drill Sheets
CC3207	Gr. 3-5 Algebra Drill Sheets
CC3208	Gr. 3-5 Geometry Drill Sheets
CC3209	Gr. 3-5 Measurement Drill Sheets
CC3210	Gr. 3-5 Data Analysis & Probability Drill Sheets
CC3211	Gr. 3-5 Five Strands of Math Big Book Drill Sheets
CC3212	Gr. 6-8 Number & Operations Drill Sheets
CC3213	Gr. 6-8 Algebra Drill Sheets
CC3214	Gr. 6-8 Geometry Drill Sheets
CC3215	Gr. 6-8 Measurement Drill Sheets
CC3216	Gr. 6-8 Data Analysis & Probability Drill Sheets
CC3217	Gr. 6-8 Five Strands of Math Big Book Drill Sheets
	TASK & DRILL SHEETS
CC3300	Gr. PK-2 Number & Operations Task & Drill Sheets
CC3301	Gr. PK-2 Algebra Task & Drill Sheets
CC3302	Gr. PK-2 Geometry Task & Drill Sheets
CC3303	Gr. PK-2 Measurement Task & Drill Sheets
CC3304	Gr. PK-2 Data Analysis & Probability Task & Drills
CC3306	Gr. 3-5 Number & Operations Task & Drill Sheets
CC3307	Gr. 3-5 Algebra Task & Drill Sheets
CC3308	Gr. 3-5 Geometry Task & Drill Sheets
CC3309	Gr. 3-5 Measurement Task & Drill Sheets
CC3310	Gr. 3-5 Data Analysis & Probability Task & Drills
CC3312	Gr. 6-8 Number & Operations Task & Drill Sheets
CC3313	Gr. 6-8 Algebra Task & Drill Sheets
CC3314	Gr. 6-8 Geometry Task & Drill Sheets
CC3315	Gr. 6-8 Measurement Task & Drill Sheets
CC3316	Gr. 6-8 Data Analysis & Probability Task & Drills